ASTRONAUT PUZZLES

Stella Maidment and Daniela Dogliani

QED Publishing

Editor: Alexandra Koken
Designer: Elaine Wilkinson

Copyright © QED Publishing 2013

First published in the UK in 2013
QED Publishing
A Quarto Group company
230 City Road
London EC1V 2TT

www.qed-publishing.co.uk

A catalogue record for this book is available from the British Library.

ISBN 978 1 78171 139 2

Printed in China

If you get stuck, the answers are at the back of the book!

Welcome to Outer Space!

This is Alfie the astronaut.

And this is his co-pilot, Sam.

Solve the puzzles in this book and help Alfie and Sam discover a new planet.

Look out for Rob-E the robot too. You'll find him in every picture!

Alfie and Sam are getting
ready to go into space.

4

Can you match their boots, helmets and gloves to their spacesuits?

Can you spot these things?

 a camera

two books

a rucksack

5

THREE... TWO... ONE...

BLAST OFF!

The rocket zooms into the sky.

CONTROLS

Which two controls are pointing in the same direction?

Can you spot these things?

Planet Earth

two red buttons

two torches

Suddenly, Alfie sees some strange spacecraft nearby. "They look like scooters," he says.

Which space scooter is smaller than the others?

Can you spot these things?

three stars

two satellites

shooting star

9

"They're space aliens!" gasps Sam. "And I think the smallest one wants us to follow him. Come on, let's go!"

Follow the small alien and see where he ends up. Where are each of the other aliens going?

Can you spot these things?

screwdriver

three space rocks

a flag

11

Alfie and Sam are on an alien planet!

"Obilee-gobilee!" says their new friend.

"I think that means hello," says Alfie.

Can you see three more space aliens hiding in the picture?

Can you spot these things?

three blue trees

an orange pond

two green birds

13

Alfie and Sam decide to call their new friend Zed. He shows them around his planet.

Can you spot these things?

a pink mountain

three pink plants

a space bus

14

Which path leads to the city?

Alfie and Sam are amazed by some of the creatures that live in the city.

Alfie takes lots of photographs.

Can you find four differences between the two flying creatures?

Can you spot these things?

two spiky plants

a winged snake

a space scooter

17

Then they all have lunch in Zed's home. The food looks strange, but it tastes delicious!

Alfie likes the blue things best.

18

After lunch, Zed and his friends show Alfie and Sam their favourite game.

Who do you think
is winning?

Can you spot
these things?

a hat

a rabbit

a bird's nest

21

It's time for Alfie and Sam to go home. Everyone helps the rocket prepare for lift-off.

Can you find the three tools that are missing from the toolkit?

Can you spot these things?

a ladder

a pile of screws and bolts

Alfie's camera

23

"Goodbye, and thank you," say Alfie and Sam, waving.

"Gobilee-obilee!" call their new friends, waving back.

Can you spot these things?

a galaxy

three pink stars

a UFO

Can you help the rocket reach Earth without hitting any space rocks?

Alfie and Sam can't wait to tell
everyone about their adventure.

And guess who's followed them back to Earth! Can you see him?

Can you spot these things?

three seagulls

a sailing boat   a sandcastle

27

Answers

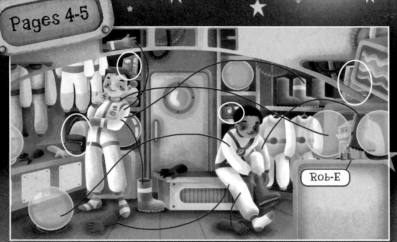

Rob-E

Follow the red lines to match Alfie and Sam's boots, helmets and gloves to their suits.

Rob-E

The two controls circled in red are pointing in the same direction.

Rob-E

The smallest space scooter is circled in red.

Rob-E

The smallest alien ends up on the purple planet. Follow the colourful lines to see where the other aliens are going!

Pages 12-13

The three hiding space aliens are circled in red.

Pages 14-15

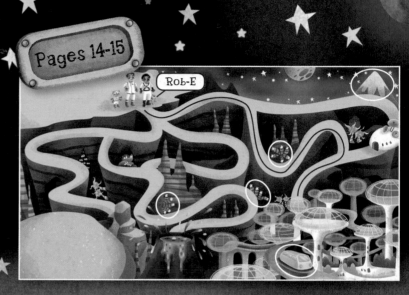

Follow the red line to get to the city.

Pages 16-17

The four differences between the flying aliens are circled in red.

Pages 18-19

Alfie's favourite foods are circled in red. They are a blue doughnut, blue ice cream and blue pizza!

Answers

Pages 20-21

Rob-E

There are more white balls from Alfie's team in the basket, so they are winning!

Pages 22-23

Rob-E

The three missing tools are circled in red.

Pages 24-25

Rob-E

Pages 26-27

Rob-E

Follow the red line to get back to Earth safely.

Zed has followed them back to Earth!
He's circled in red.

More space fun

Lunar landscape
Take a really big piece of cardboard and glue old cardboard boxes and tubes onto it to make a strange lunar landscape. Egg boxes are particularly good for this. Paint the boxes once you have stuck them firmly in place.

Astronaut day!
Dress up as an astronaut for the day! Make a helmet by covering a big balloon with papier mâché. Leave it to dry overnight, then cut holes for your head and for your face. Paint the helmet and wear it with a tracksuit, gloves and boots. Maybe you could even have an astronaut-themed party!

Star and planet biscuits
Ask an adult to help you make some biscuit dough and help you cut it into planet and star shapes. Once the biscuits are baked and cooled you can decorate them with icing, sprinkles or little coloured sweets.

Make funny aliens
Cut the heads and the bodies of people and animals from old magazines, then put them together in funny combinations. Stick them on a sheet of paper and give them silly alien names.